4 ...DATA FILE... THE HULK™
6 "BY BANNER BETRAYED!"
11 COLOUR BLAST!
12 ...DATA FILE CAPTAIN AMERICA™
19 ULTIMATE X-CHANGE!
26 INSIDE THE HELICARRIER!
32 X-MANSION ASSAULT!
34 NEIGHBOURHOOD THREAT!
41 X-TRAORDINARY POWER!
D0120300
M HARM
49 MARVEL MASTERPIECE
50 INSIDE THE X-MANSION!
52 ...DATA FILE... THE SENTINELS™
53 ...DATA FILE... THE MIGHTY THOR™
54 THE WAR OF THE TROLLS
62 ANSWERS
£7.99

The Hulk – 1000 pounds of rippling muscle with a hair-trigger temper! But is he really a rampaging menace or simply a misunderstood monster? Decide for yourselves as we reveal all his secrets!

HULK IS THE STRONGEST ONE THERE IS!

Dr. Bruce Banner transforms into the Hulk whenever he gets angry or stressed.

He regularly practises *ancient meditation techniques* to stay calm, but even these can't completely control his inner *rage.*

POWER RANKING:

STRENGTH:	20
SPEED:	14
INTELLIGENCE:	5
AGILITY:	7
POWERS:	18

Even though he's pretty lacking in the brains department, the Hulk has a natural cunning that makes him a dangerously unpredictable fighter.

THE ORIGINS OF... THE HULK™

DR. BRUCE BANNER WORKED FOR THE US MILITARY HELPING THEM TO DEVELOP A NEW EXPERIMENTAL WEAPON...
...THE GAMMA BOMB!
MY BOMB BETTER WORK BANNER -- OR ELSE!
BUT ON THE DAY OF THE FIRST TEST, HIS LIFE CHANGED FOREVER!

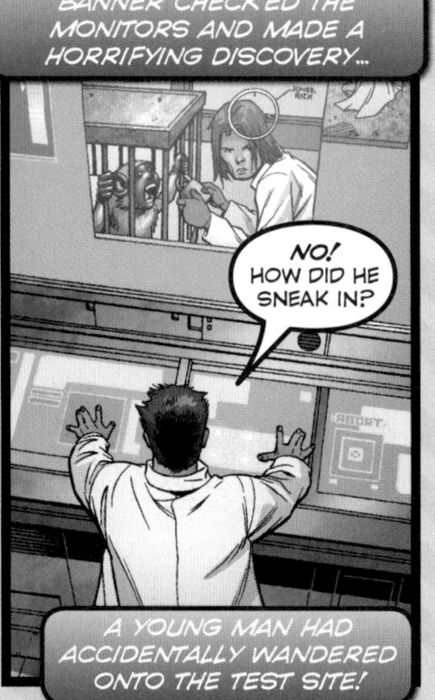

MINUTES BEFORE DETONATION, BANNER CHECKED THE MONITORS AND MADE A HORRIFYING DISCOVERY...
NO! HOW DID HE SNEAK IN?
A YOUNG MAN HAD ACCIDENTALLY WANDERED ONTO THE TEST SITE!

DISREGARDING HIS OWN SAFETY, BANNER JUMPED IN A JEEP AND SPED TO THE RESCUE!
IF I DON'T REACH HIM IN TIME, HE'LL BE VAPORISED BY THE BLAST!

HULK GO BOOM!

By smashing his *huge hands* together, Hulk can create a SONIC BOOM strong enough to floor his foes!

HULK FACTS:

His skin is so tough, even armour-piercing bullets bounce right off it!

FACT FILE: HULK™

REAL NAME: DR BRUCE BANNER
HEIGHT: 7′
WEIGHT: 1040 LBS
EYES: GREEN
HAIR: GREEN
POWERS / ABILITIES: SUPER STRENGTH AND REGENERATION

HULK FACTS:

The angrier Hulk gets, the stronger he becomes!

HULK FACTS:

The Hulk's huge leg muscles allow him to leap up to 3 miles in a single jump!

AS THE SMOKE CLEARED THE BOMB'S EFFECTS BECAME APPARENT...

BANNER HAD BEEN TRANSFORMED INTO A GREEN-SKINNED, SUPER STRONG, 7-FOOT-TALL MONSTER.
HE HAD BECOME -- THE HULK!

BANNER NOW SPENDS HIS LIFE ON THE RUN FROM THE US MILITARY...
STRUGGLING TO LIVE IN PEACE, OR RISK UNLEASHING THE MONSTER WITHIN!

"BY BANNER BETRAYED!"
THE TIME: THE DAWN OF THE AGE OF HEROES.
THE PLACE: THE AMERICAN SOUTHWEST.
THE OCCASION: A MEETING BETWEEN EARTH'S MIGHTIEST HEROES AND A CERTAIN GREEN-SKINNED GOLIATH!
THE OUTLOOK: ACTION AND ANGST IN THE MIGHTY MARVEL MANNER!
THERE'S NO NEED TO FIGHT, HULK! WE'VE BEEN TRACKING YOU FOR DAYS AND JUST WANT TO TALK.
FORGET IT, YOU OVERGROWN OAF! I HAVEN'T FORGOTTEN THAT YOU LAME-BRAINED LOSERS CONNED ME INTO JOINING YOUR STUPID TEAM--
--AND THEN TURNED AGAINST ME WITHOUT A SECOND THOUGHT!
IF I REMEMBER CORRECTLY, YOU DECIDED TO QUIT.
SAVE YOUR BREATH, IRON MAN. IF HE'S NOT GOING TO COOPERATE, THERE'S NO POINT IN ARGUING.
WE'LL HAVE TO TAKE HIM DOWN LIKE WE PRACTISED...
"TWO-FISTED" TOM DEFALCO & "RAMPAGING" RON FRENZ PLOT, SCRIPT & PENCILS
"OUR PAL" SAL BUSCEMA FINISHED ART
"CRAZY" CHRIS ELIOPOULOS LETTERS
"NICE" NICK FILARDI COLORS
"LIGHTNING QUICK" LEE WEEKS & "AWESOME" ANDY TROY COVER ART
JAKE "THE SNAKE" THOMAS ASSISTANT EDITOR
"BATTLING" BILL ROSEMANN EDITOR
AXEL "THE AXE MAN" ALONSO EDITOR IN CHIEF
"JOLTIN'" JOE QUESADA CHIEF CREATIVE OFFICER
"DANGEROUS" DAN BUCKLEY PUBLISHER
"AMAZING" ALAN FINE EXEC. PRODUCER
SPECIAL THANKS TO TOM BRENNAN & TOM BREVOORT

PAGE 6

NOW!
FEW MORTALS HAVE E'ER PRESUMED TO COMMAND THE SON OF ODIN--
--BUT EAGERLY DOES THOR HEED THE WORD OF CAPTAIN AMERICA!
HITTING THE HULK SIMULTANEOUSLY MAY HAVE SOUNDED LIKE A GOOD IDEA--
--BUT IT ISN'T WORKING!
H-HE SEEMS STRONGER THAN EVER!
THAT'S BECAUSE HIS STRENGTH INCREASES AS HE GETS ANGRIER.
FEAR NOT, RICK JONES! NO POWER ON EARTH CAN BREAK OUR COMBINED GRIP.
WE FINALLY GOT HIM UNDER CONTROL, CAP.
I HEAR YOU LOUD AND CLEAR, IRON MAN.
I'VE ALREADY SIGNALED THE ARMY TO BRING IN THOSE SPECIAL RESTRAINTS THAT TONY STARK DESIGNED FOR US.
THE HULK IS SO TERRIFYING--
--EVEN WHEN HE'S HELPLESS!
WANNA KNOW SOMETHING REALLY TERRIFYING, WASP?
THE HULK IS NEVER HELPLESS!
QUOOOM!

JANET, LOOK OUT!
TOO LATE! HE'S ALREADY PUNTED THAT CHUNK OF GRANITE RIGHT AT HER!
NOT TO WORRY, GENTLEMEN!
THE WONDROUS WASP WON'T BE INTIMIDATED BY A POINTLESS TANTRUM.
HEADS UP! BASED ON THAT BOULDER'S TRAJECTORY, THE HULK MAY BE CRAFTIER THAN HE LOOKS.
KRAKT!
RRRRRRRRRRRRRRRRRRRR
OH, NO! NO!
WASP, EVASIVE MANOEUVRE #17!
JANET--!
GIANT-MAN-- DON'T LET GO!
GO! GO! GO!
I'M RIGHT BEHIND YOU.
ARE YOU ALWAYS SO COOL UNDER FIRE, CAP?
ONLY WHEN LIVES ARE AT STAKE!

STUPID--
PUNY--
FOOLS!
QWA-TWOOOM!
IT'S ABOUT TIME YOU REALISED--
NOTHING CAN STOP THE HULK!
STOP HOUNDING ME--
--OR I WON'T BE SO GENTLE NEXT TIME.
THIS IS MY FAULT! IF I HADN'T RUSHED TO JAN'S AID--!
AT EASE, HIGH POCKETS! NO ONE CAN BLAME YOU FOR FOLLOWING YOUR HEART.
THOUGH THE HULK CAN COVER MILES WITH EACH BOUND, HE CANNOT ESCAPE THE GOD OF THUNDER.
FORGET IT, THOR! WE CAN ALWAYS FIND HIM LATER...
AFTER WE DEVISE ANOTHER PLAN.
AFTER ALL, WE'RE JUST TRYING TO CONVINCE HIM TO FORGET THE PAST AND COME BACK TO THE AVENGERS.
I'M BEGINNING TO DOUBT OUR CHANCES OF SUCCESS, CAP.
IT'S PRETTY OBVIOUS--

CONTINUED ON PAGE 14

COLOUR BLAST!
Okay, tech-heads, it's time to show-off your colouring skills, so grab your pens and pencils and add a splash of colour to this awesome picture of the invincible Iron Man!

Ever since the dark days of World War 2, Captain America has courageously fought to protect the world from danger. Read on to find out all about him!

With his physical abilities **boosted** by a secret experimental serum, Steve Rogers was the U.S.A.'s secret weapon during World War 2. As Captain America, he undertook many dangerous missions to help the allied forces defeat the **Nazi scourge**.

Tragedy struck in 1945 when Cap was seemingly killed whilst trying to defuse an **experimental drone missile** created by the evil **Baron Zemo**. The missile exploded over the North Atlantic Ocean, sending Cap's body plunging into the **icy depths** below.

Years later his body was found **entombed** in a block of ice. Somehow the experimental serum had kept him in a state of **perfect hibernation**.

Once thawed out, Cap found himself in a world **unrecognizable** to the one he'd known in the past. However, he still stood by his duty to **uphold freedom and liberty**, and now protects a **whole new generation** from Super Villain threats.

DID YOU KNOW?

During World War 2, Cap had a teenage sidekick called Bucky. Though Bucky was thought killed on Cap's final mission, he re-surfaced years later as the Winter Soldier!

CONTINUED FROM PAGE 10

KEEP ALERT! THE HULK IS FAR MORE FAMILIAR WITH THESE CANYONS THAN WE ARE--
--AND HE WON'T HESITATE TO LAUNCH A SNEAK ATTACK.
RICK, I WANT YOU TO STAY ON THE SIDELINES WITH THE SOLDIERS WHEN WE CATCH UP TO THE HULK.
I'M ALREADY RESPONSIBLE FOR THE DEATH OF ONE PARTNER--
--AND I CAN'T TAKE THE RESPONSIBILITY FOR PUTTING YOU IN HARM'S WAY.
IT'S NOT YOUR DECISION, CAP.
YOU'VE MADE IT PRETTY CLEAR THAT YOU DON'T WANT ME AS A PARTNER.
BESIDES, YOU'RE NOT THE ONLY ONE HAUNTED BY THE GALLOPING GUILTS.
THE HULK WOULDN'T EVEN EXIST IF HE HADN'T RISKED HIS LIFE TO SAVE MINE.
HOLD UP, PEOPLE! WE'RE CLOSING IN ON OUR QUARRY.
BASED ON THESE HEAT SIGNATURES, THE HULK PASSED THIS WAY ONLY A FEW MINUTES AGO AND MAY BE NEARBY.
COYOTE ONE, DO YOU COPY?
COME IN, COYOTE ONE.
PROBLEM, SOLDIER?
POSSIBLY, SIR.
COYOTE ONE IS ON POINT AND ISN'T RESPONDING TO MY--

INCOMING--!
AVENGERS ASSEMBLE!
'TIS SORCERY MOST FOUL!
LOOKS LIKE THE HULK HAS ALLIED HIMSELF WITH OUR OLD ENEMY BARON ZEMO AND HIS FRIENDS.
RICK, TELL THE SOLDIERS TO FALL BACK--
--WHILE WE SET UP A DEFENSIVE PERIMETER.
LONG HAS MY ALMIGHTY BATTLE-AXE THIRSTED FOR YOUR BLOOD!
NOW SHALL THE EXECUTIONER CLAIM HIS RIGHTEOUS VENGEANCE!
MANY HAVE CHALLENGED THE GOD OF THUNDER...
FEW HAVE EVER SURVIVED HIS RAGING STORM!
DON'T FORCE ME TO HURT YOU, ENCHANTRESS!
SURRENDER NOW AND I PROMISE TO-- ARRRGH!
THERE ARE TIMES FOR CHIVALRY, HANK.
THIS ISN'T ONE OF THEM.
JUST WATCH ME FLATTEN THAT VICIOUS VIXEN!
IF MY MAGIC CAN STOP YOUR TOWERING COMPANION--
--IT CAN CERTAINLY DEFEAT A TROUBLESOME INSECT LIKE YOU.

BWADOOOM!
YOU'RE GOING TO HAVE TO HIT HARDER THAN THAT, SHELLHEAD.
A WHOLE LOT HARDER!
ONLY IF YOU INSIST--!
I'D RATHER TRY TO REASON WITH YOU.
COME BACK TO THE AVENGERS AND ALLOW US TO HELP YOU.
YEAH, HELP ME INTO THOSE "SPECIAL RESTRAINTS DESIGNED BY TONY STARK"?!
OKAY, WE'LL PLAY THIS YOUR WAY.
YOU MAY THINK YOUR BRAINS AND TECHNOLOGY TRUMPS MY BRAWN AND SAVAGERY--
--BUT TIME WORKS IN MY FAVOUR!
W-WHAT DO YOU MEAN?

CONTINUED ON PAGE 20

ULTIMATE X-CHANGE!

Take cover, Marvelites! The Hulk is on the rampage and only Colossus and Wolverine are standing in his way! Can help the two X-Men stop the Hulkster by spotting the ten differences between these two pictures?

RAARGH! HULK SMASH TIN-MAN AND CLAW-MAN!
JEEZ -- AND PEOPLE TELL ME I GOT ANGER MANAGEMENT ISSUES...

ANSWERS: 1 – Washing line, 2 – Gnome in bottom right corner, 3 – Shovel in Hulk's hand, 4 – Bird table behind Wolverine, 5 – Spider's web, 6 – Hulk's hair, 7 – Wolverine's hat, 8 – Hulk's trousers, 9 – Pigeon, 10 – Extra vine at top.

CONTINUED FROM PAGE 18

"--EVEN AS MY UNDERLINGS OBLITERATE YOUR CURRENT TEAMMATES!"
KEEP YOUR HANDS OFF GIANT-MAN, YOU SUPERNATURAL SCOUNDREL!
IN CASE YOU HAVEN'T GUESSED, HE'S ALREADY SPOKEN FOR.
TZING! TZING! TZING!
THANKS FOR DISTRACTING THE ENCHANTRESS, JAN--
--BUT I CAN'T BREAK FREE OF THESE LIVING VINES SHE SICCED ON ME.
I GUESS I'M JUST GOING TO HAVE TO GROW OUT OF THIS PROBLEM!
YIIII!
AWAY, YOU BRAZEN BUG-WOMAN!
NOW SHALL YOU PAY FOR YOUR INTOLERABLE IMPUDENCE!
NOW SHALL YOU SUFFER A TORMENT SO TERRIBLE THAT YOU WILL BEG FOR THE SWEET EMBRACE OF HELA, GODDESS OF DEATH.
YOU'D BETTER LEAVE THE WASP ALONE--
--OR YOU'LL HAVE A BIG PROBLEM!
ARE YOU INSANE?!?
HOW DARE YOU--A MERE MORTAL--THREATEN ME?!
PAGE 21

I AM
ASGARD, WHOSE MASTERY OF MAGIC IS UNEQUALED BY ALL SAVE A PRECIOUS FEW.
WHERE I COME FROM--
--EVEN GIANTS FEAR TO TREAD!
WHAM!
WHOOOOM!
LAY DOWN YOUR WEAPON, SKURGE.
LET THIS BATTLE CEASE.
'TIS MOST UNSEEMLY FOR TWO IMMORTALS TO FIGHT AT THE BEQUEST OF ONE SUCH AS BARON ZEMO.
HOW LITTLE YOU KNOW OF THE EXECUTIONER, ODINSON.
I STRIKE BECAUSE YOUR FATHER BANISHED ME FROM THE REALM ETERNAL--
--AND YOU HAVE STOLEN THE HEART OF THE ONLY GODDESS I HAVE EVER LOVED.
BUT THE ENCHANTRESS MEANS NOTHING TO ME.
KA-ZAK!
THUS MUST I STRIKE FOR HER HONOUR AS WELL AS MY OWN!

SO BE IT!
WHEN REASON FAILS, STRENGTH MUST SUFFICE.
THOUGH YOUR FABLED BATTLE-AXE CAN CLEAVE THROUGH ALMOST ANY OBJECT--
--STILL DOES ITS POWER PALE BEFORE MJOLNIR, THE ALMIGHTY HAMMER OF THOR!
HURLED AM I TOWARD THE JAGGED ROCKS BELOW--!
IF THIS IS FATED TO BE MY FINAL BATTLE, CONTENT AM I TO DIE IN THE SERVICE OF MY BELOVED AMORA.
A GREATER FOOL I HAVE NE'ER KNOWN!
NONE SHALL DIE WHEN THOR CAN ACT.
WHERE THERE IS LIFE, THERE IS HOPE!
THERE COULD STILL COME A DAY WHEN MY ALL-POWERFUL FATHER WELCOMES YOU BACK TO ASGARD.
YOU SHOULD HAVE LET ME DIE, THUNDER GOD.
WHILE THE EXECUTIONER BREATHES--
"--THE AVENGERS HAVE CAUSE TO FEAR!"
PWA-TANGGGG!
P-POWER RUNNING LOW...
CAN'T TAKE MUCH MORE PUNISHMENT!

I WARNED YOU, YOU BOLT-BRAINED BOZO!
NO ONE CAN BEAT ME.
YOU'RE HEADED FOR THE SCRAP HEAP--
--COURTESY OF THE HULK!
MY ONLY HOPE IS TO DIVERT MY REMAINING RESERVES TO MY REPULSORS BEFORE HE--
SKRRRUTCHHHHH!
SAY GOODNIGHT, TIN MAN!
WITHOUT YOUR MAIN BATTERY, YOU'RE JUST A PILE OF USELESS METAL.
HEY, MR. GREEN GENES--!
KARZAAAM!
YOU TALK TOO MUCH.
YOUR STRENGTH AND AGILITY ARE AS IMPRESSIVE AS EVER, MY DEAR CAPTAIN--
--BUT MY TECHNOLOGY IS FAR SUPERIOR!
NOT EVEN CAP CAN KEEP THIS PACE.
MAYBE WE CAN SNEAK BEHIND ZEMO AND CATCH HIM BY SURPRISE.

CONTINUED ON PAGE 28

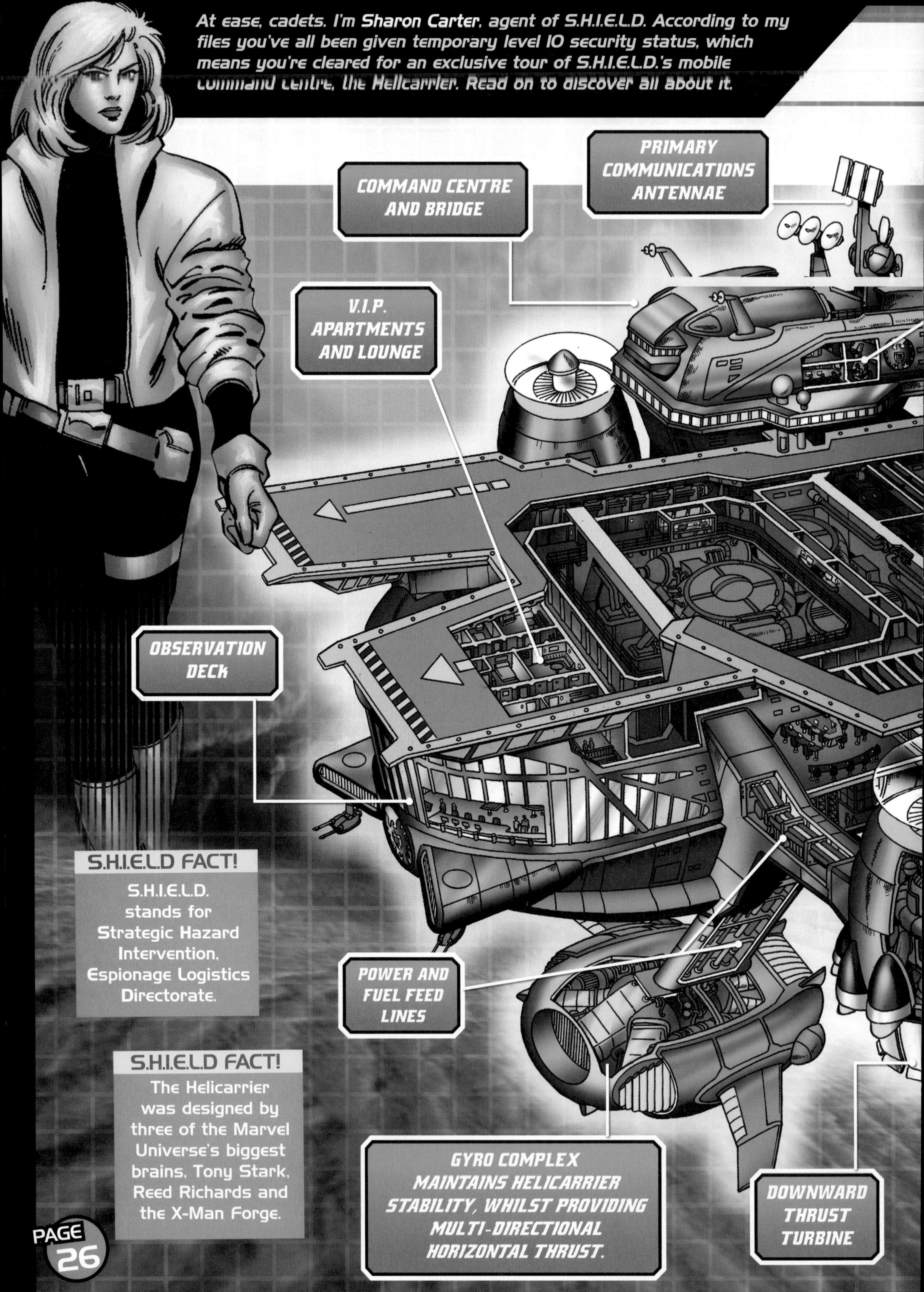
At ease, cadets. I'm Sharon Carter, agent of S.H.I.E.L.D. According to my files you've all been given temporary level 10 security status, which means you're cleared for an exclusive tour of S.H.I.E.L.D.'s mobile command centre, the Helicarrier. Read on to discover all about it.
COMMAND CENTRE AND BRIDGE
PRIMARY COMMUNICATIONS ANTENNAE
V.I.P. APARTMENTS AND LOUNGE
OBSERVATION DECK
POWER AND FUEL FEED LINES
GYRO COMPLEX MAINTAINS HELICARRIER STABILITY, WHILST PROVIDING MULTI-DIRECTIONAL HORIZONTAL THRUST.
DOWNWARD THRUST TURBINE
S.H.I.E.L.D FACT!
S.H.I.E.L.D. stands for Strategic Hazard Intervention, Espionage Logistics Directorate.
S.H.I.E.L.D FACT!
The Helicarrier was designed by three of the Marvel Universe's biggest brains, Tony Stark, Reed Richards and the X-Man Forge.

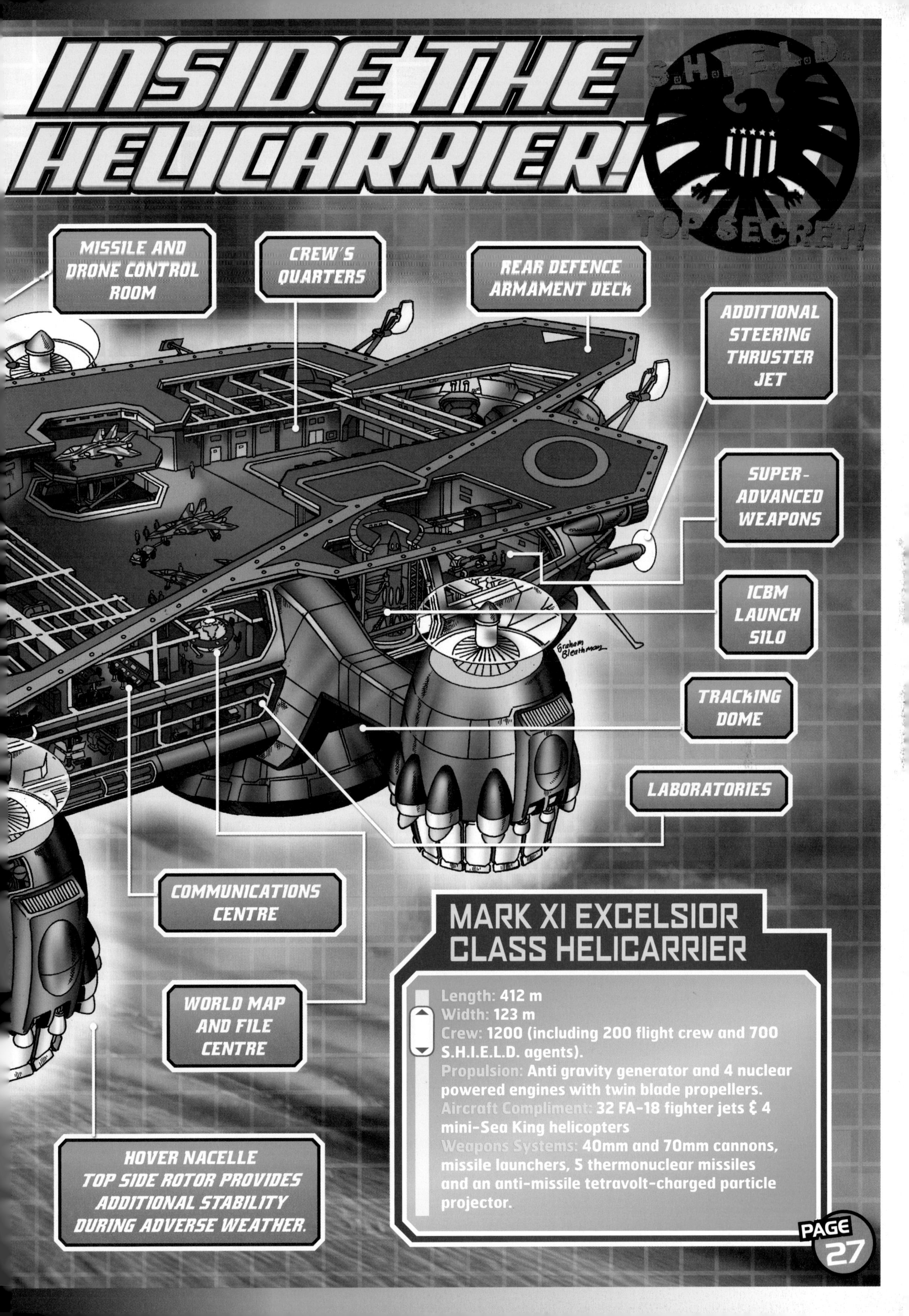
INSIDE THE HELICARRIER!
S.H.I.E.L.D.
TOP SECRET!
MISSILE AND DRONE CONTROL ROOM
CREW'S QUARTERS
REAR DEFENCE ARMAMENT DECK
ADDITIONAL STEERING THRUSTER JET
SUPER-ADVANCED WEAPONS
ICBM LAUNCH SILO
TRACKING DOME
LABORATORIES
COMMUNICATIONS CENTRE
WORLD MAP AND FILE CENTRE
HOVER NACELLE
TOP SIDE ROTOR PROVIDES ADDITIONAL STABILITY DURING ADVERSE WEATHER.
MARK XI EXCELSIOR CLASS HELICARRIER
Length: 412 m
Width: 123 m
Crew: 1200 (including 200 flight crew and 700 S.H.I.E.L.D. agents).
Propulsion: Anti gravity generator and 4 nuclear powered engines with twin blade propellers.
Aircraft Compliment: 32 FA-18 fighter jets & 4 mini-Sea King helicopters
Weapons Systems: 40mm and 70mm cannons, missile launchers, 5 thermonuclear missiles and an anti-missile tetravolt-charged particle projector.
PAGE 27

CONTINUED FROM PAGE 25

OD'S BLOOD! THE VERY EARTH TREMBLES BENEATH MY FEET.
I MUST LEARN THE CAUSE OF THIS MOST UNSETTLING DISTURBANCE AFTER I HAVE HUMBLED THE GIANT ONE.
NEVER AGAIN WILL HE PRESUME TO CHALLENGE THE ENCHANTRESS OR--
ANTS! THOUSANDS OF THEM ARE ATTACKING WITHOUT MERCY!
YOU THINK THAT'S PAINFUL?
WAIT UNTIL YOU GET A LOAD OF MY STING!
AAAYIIII!
AMORA!
NO DANGER CAN BEFALL YOU WHILE THE EXECUTIONER STANDS!
I AM HERE, MY LOVE.
THE TIDE HAS TURNED AGAINST US.
WE MUST FLEE WHILE WE STILL CAN.
GOOD RIDDANCE TO BAD RUBBISH IF YOU ASK ME!
HOW ARE YOU DOING, BLUE-EYES?
A LOT BETTER... THANKS TO YOU!
PAGE 29

IT SORELY GRIEVES ME TO ADMIT DEFEAT, BUT I MUST CAST A SPELL THAT WILL SEND US TO SAFETY--
"--ALONG WITH YOUR DEADLY BATTLE-AXE-
"--AND OUR MORTAL ALLY!"
FIGURES THEY'D DESERT ME.
NOT THAT IT MATTERS.
I'M DONE WITH THAT BUNCH, ANYWAY.
WHERE THE HULK TRAVELS, HE GOES ALONE!
HULK, WAIT--!
I WANTED TO TALK-- TO THANK YOU!
FORGET IT, RICK.
WITH THOSE INCREDIBLE LEG MUSCLES OF HIS, HE'S ALREADY MILES AWAY.
STORY OF MY LIFE.
I'M ALWAYS LEFT BEHIND.
PAGE 30

ZEMO AND THE OTHERS MAY HAVE ESCAPED FOR THE MOMENT, BUT THE HULK CAN EASILY BE FOLLOWED.
WHAT'S THE POINT, THOR?
IRON MAN AND GIANT-MAN ARE TEMPORARILY OUT OF COMMISSION AND I COULD USE A REST MYSELF.
THE GOD OF THUNDER COULD EASILY DEFEAT THE MONSTER ON HIS OWN.
I DON'T DOUBT YOU.
BUT I'M STARTING TO FEEL SORRY FOR THE HULK.
WHEN IT REALLY COUNTED, HE CAME THROUGH FOR RICK.
IT'S OBVIOUS THAT HE STILL HAS FEELINGS FOR THE BOY.
"IT'S A HORRIBLE THING TO LOSE A PARTNER--TO SUDDENLY BE CAST ALONE AND ADRIFT!
"I CAN'T EVEN IMAGINE THE TERRIBLE TRAGEDY OF BEING THE MAN TRAPPED WITHIN THE MONSTER--
"--CALLED THE HULK!"

X-MEN

This is Professor X of the X-Men. I am using **Cerebra** to send an *urgent telepathic message* to all mutant allies. The X-Mansion is under **attack** from a new form of Sentinel robots and we need your help to find them all. Good luck – the **fate** of the X-Men rests on your shoulders!

See if you can spot how many of each of these are hiding in the X-Mansion's grounds.

Can you track down each of the X-Men as well?

ANGEL

X-MANSION ASSAULT!
SENTINELS - ENGAGE ACTIVE CAMOUFLAGE!
FINISH
START
Cyclops needs to make his way through the maze to meet up with the other X-Men. Can you work out which way he should go?
GAMBIT
NIGHTCRAWLER
STORM
COLOSSUS
WOLVERINE
ROGUE
BEAST
PAGE 33
Answers: 12 Sentinels. 9 X-Communicators

NO, NOT
RESIST...
HAVE TO...
DOCTOR CURTIS CONNORS
NARGH!
NEIGHBOURHOOD THREAT!
SCRIPT: FERG HANDLEY
PENCILS: CARLOS GOMEZ
INKS: GARY ERSKINE
COLOUR: JUNIOR TOMLIN
LETTERING: ROBERT CHARLES
HSSS...
LATER.
BUT IT'LL BE FUN, PETEY. COME ON, WHERE'S YOUR SENSE OF ADVENTURE?
FINE, MARY JANE, SATURDAY IT IS. BUT YOU'D BETTER HAVE THE EMERGENCY ROOM ON STANDBY...
...'COS WHEN IT COMES TO ICE SKATING, I'M ABOUT AS GRACEFUL AS A BABY RHINO.
NOW THERE'S AN INTERESTING IMAGE. SERIOUSLY THOUGH, YOU'LL BE FINE.
SURE HOPE SO, MJ.
ANYHOW, I'D BETTER SAY GOOD NIGHT TO AUNT MAY. CALL YOU TOMORROW?
YOU BETCHA, TIGER.

ARE YOU SURE YOU DON'T WANT A MUG, PETER DEAR?
THANKS, BUT I'D BETTER PASS.
COCOA ALWAYS MAKES ME DROWSY, AND I'VE STILL GOT A BUNCH OF COURSE WORK TO GET THROUGH.
BLESS HER, SHE REALLY DOES LOOK OUT FOR ME. BUT I REALLY NEED TO HIT THE BOOKS. AND I DO...
UNTIL...
SPIDER-SENSE! BUT SURELY I'M NOT IN DANGER IN MY OWN HOME...
WHOA!
BLINK OF AN EYE AND IT'S GONE.
BUT SOMETHING'S OUT THERE...
...SO I DO THE FASTEST QUICK CHANGE SINCE QUICKSILVER SPILT HOT COFFEE ON HIS BEST COSTUME...
...AND THERE HE IS...
...THE LIZARD!
GET OUT HERE, PARKER! NOW, OR I'M COMING IN!
WHAT?!! EVEN DOC CONNORS DOESN'T KNOW MY REAL IDENTITY...

...AND HE'S A FRIEND OF MINE. SEE, THE DOC LOST HIS ARM A WHILE BACK...
...AND WHEN HE TRIED EXPERIMENTING WITH REPTILE DNA TO GROW IT BACK, THINGS WENT WRONG - - SO WHENEVER HE'S STRESSED, HE TURNS INTO TOOTHSOME MACNASTY HERE.
OKAY, FIRST THINGS FIRST. GOTTA GET HIM AWAY FROM THE HOUSE AND AUNT MAY...
HRRRK!
SLAAAM
SSSPIDER-MAN! I WANTED PARKER, BUT YOU WILL DO FOR NOW- -
GLUBB
...PREFERABLY, WITHOUT WAKING UP THE NEIGHBOURS!
NOW WHY DON'T WE FIND YOU A NICE ROCK TO SLITHER UNDER?
NOTHING FANCY MIND, JUST A- -
THWAAAAM
UNGH!
NOW NORMALLY, I END UP FORCING ANTI-SERUM DOWN OL' SNAPPY'S CHOPS AND TURNING HIM BACK TO CONNORS. BUT HIS LAB'S WAY ACROSS TOWN...
...WHICH MAKES THINGS A TAD TRICKY.
COURSE, THERE IS ANOTHER WAY. BUT HOW AM I GOING TO...?
WAIT, THAT'S IT! THANKS, MJ - - YOU'LL NEVER KNOW IT, BUT YOU'VE GIVEN ME AN IDEA HERE!

NOW I JUST NEED TO GET HIM MOVING. SO LET'S TRY THE SUBTLE APPROACH...
LOOKING A BIT FLABBY THERE, FANG-FACE.
LIKE, HAVEN'T I WARNED YOU ABOUT MOUSEY SNACKS BETWEEN MEALS?
YOU'LL SSSUFFER FOR THAT, YOU COSSSTUMED APELING!
MAN, HE'S FAST. BUT I KNOW THIS AREA INSIDE OUT...
...AND I MANAGE TO STAY ONE SWING AHEAD. WELL, FOR MOST OF THE TIME...
YEEESH, SOMEBODY AIN'T FLOSSING!
KLAAAAK
HONEST, DUDE - - WITH CHOPPERS LIKE THOSE, YOU'VE DEFINITELY GOTTA STEP UP THE DENTAL HYGIENE!
ONE SSSLIP, SSSPIDER-MAN... ONE SSSLIP AND YOU'RE MINE!
GEE, NOW THERE'S SOMETHING TO LOOK FORWARD TO.
AND SO IT GOES, THROUGH THE STREETS AND BACK YARDS...
...THEN BINGO, THERE IT IS.
COURSE, IT'S ALL LOCKED UP FOR THE NIGHT...
...SO...
KRAAANCH
WHAT IN THE NAME OF...?
SPIDER-MAN!
DARN, THESE THREADS ARE SUCH A GIVE-AWAY.

SERIOUSLY THOUGH, BUDDY, YOU REALLY OUGHT TO TAKE A BREAK ROUND ABOUT NOW.
NO WAY, BUSTER. I DON'T LEAVE MY POST FOR NUTHIN', AND THAT'S- -
ARGH!
OKAY, THAT'S CLEARED THE DECKS. SO...
...JUST A LITTLE BIT FURTHER...
YOU MIGHT HAVE ELUDED ME OUTSSSIDE, SSSPIDER-MAN - - BUT NOT IN HERE!
SHUCKS, NOW YOU TELL ME!
...AND HERE WE ARE!
STILL NOT QUITE COLD ENOUGH THOUGH...
BUT TURNING ON THE REFRIGERATION FANS OUGHT TO DO THE TRICK...
CLICK

WRRRR
WRRRR
NOOO! YOU SSSNEAKING MAMMAL SSSPAWN!
DON'T BE SORE, LIZZY, EVERYONE'S GOTTA CHILL OUT SOMETIME!
METABOLISSSM SSSLOWING... MUSSST ESSSCAPE!
WHAT? AFTER I'VE GONE TO ALL THIS TROUBLE?
NOOO!!!
THAT'S THE ARENA SEALED OFF. NOW I JUST GOTTA LET NATURE TAKE ITS COURSE...
MACHINERY... MUSSST DESTROY...
KLAAAAW
OH NO YOU DON'T, SPARKY!
THUNNNNK
THERE'S A FEW MORE CLOSE SHAVES, BUT HE'S DEFINITELY GETTING WEAKER. AND FINALLY...
SEE, REPTILES GO DORMANT WHEN IT'S TOO COLD - - GIANT MONSTER LIZARDS INCLUDED.
FEELING A BIT NIPPY MYSELF, MIND...
...SSS...

...BUT IT'S WORTH IT TO HAVE THE DOC BACK TO NORMAL.
STILL PUZZLED ABOUT THE LIZARD COMING AFTER ME AT HOME THOUGH...
...UNTIL WE REACH CONNORS' LAB, THAT IS...
SAY, WHAT'S THIS?
AND WHY'S IT GOT PETER PARKER'S NAME AND DETAILS ON IT?
IT'S A CONTACT SHEET, SPIDER-MAN.
EVERYONE ON IT'S HELPED ME SEARCH FOR A CURE AT SOME STAGE, PETER ESPECIALLY.
AND A CURE'S THE LAST THING THE LIZARD WANTS... SO HE DECIDED TO TAKE OUT THE ENTIRE LIST, STARTING WITH THE NEAREST ADDRESS!
I SUPPOSE HE MUST HAVE.
SORRY, SPIDER-MAN, THAT WAS CARELESS OF ME.
CARELESS DOESN'T EVEN START TO COVER IT, DOC.
YOU PUT A LOT OF PEOPLE IN DANGER...
...AND IF I HADN'T HAPPENED TO BE IN PARKER'S NEIGHBOURHOOD TONIGHT, THE GUY WOULD BE DEAD BY NOW.
NO POINT IN SAYING ANY MORE, HE'S FEELING BAD ENOUGH AS IT IS. SO I HELP HIM CLEAR UP THE MESS...
...THEN IT'S TIME FOR ME TO GET GOING. SECRET IDENTITY'S STILL SAFE, SO THAT'S SOMETHING...
...AND I CAN'T HELP THINKING THAT SURE, BEING SPIDER-MAN'S A CURSE SOMETIMES...
...BUT ALL IN ALL, IT COULD HAVE BEEN A WHOLE LOT WORSE.
THE END.

X-TRAORDINARY
POWER!
X MISSION
No matter what the danger, the X-Men are always ready to help young mutants who are in peril. Prove you're the ultimate X-fan by finding the names of these X-Men in the giant-sized word grid below. Good luck!
H H D S H A D O W C A T H W
W C F H Y H P H H H H C H F
F O J E L E F E E E E Y E H
G L L Y U Y F Y U Y Y C Y I
D O I V J I I G I I I L I P
H S O O E O O O F S T O R M
U S D L M R L L N L L P H L
P U J D M D I D Y D D S U D
L S L A A A F N E A G A R N
W C U C F C F C E C A C E I
Q G F G R B H G G G M G S G
A H E H O H I H N H B H A H
S F R F S F F S M F I F V T
F I D D T D B D H D T D N C
H C P R O F E S S O R X H R
k E A U U U A k U k P U Y A
Y M E B E E S E E L E E O W
F A G G L G T F G P G G L L
J N M M M E M H M G M M P E
Y T k T k H F A N G E L Q R
PROFESSOR X
CYCLOPS
BEAST
WOLVERINE
ANGEL
STORM
COLOSSUS
NIGHTCRAWLER
EMMA FROST
SHADOWCAT
ICEMAN
ROGUE
GAMBIT
BISHOP
CABLE
PAGE 41

...MOBILE CEREBRO PROGRAMME ONLINE...
...UNCATALOGUED MUTANT BIO-PATTERN DETECTED...
...UNCATALOGUED MUTANT IN DANGER...
SAFE FROM HARM
...LOCATION: 15 KILOMETRES WEST OF AMSTERDAM...
SCRIPT: JAMES PEATY PENCILS: NEIL EDWARDS
INKS: IAN SHARMAN COLOURS: ADRIAN SALMON
LETTERING: TIM WARRAN-SMITH
...CO-ORDINATE UPLOAD TO X-JET IN PROGRESS...
I'M HERE FOR THE MEETING.
ERRR... HELLO?!?
ARE YOU BARNELL?
THAT'S RIGHT.
BARNELL BOHUSK, SIR.
ARGH!
FWASH
HA! HE NEARLY FLEW!
VERHOEVEN'S RIGHT, MR SNEIJDER.
IT WAS ALMOST CUTE THE WAY HE TRIED TO FLAP HIS ARMS.
UGGGHHH...
CUTE?
HE ISN'T CUTE, CARRIE...

...HE'S DISGUSTING!
WHO... WHO ARE YOU?
WE'RE THE PEOPLE YOU WERE COMING TO MEET.
THE 'SECRET SOCIETY OF DUTCH MUTANTS'.
THE GROUP YOU CONTACTED ONLINE WHO WERE GOING TO HELP MAKE YOU FEEL JUST THAT LITTLE BIT LESS 'DIFFERENT'.
EXCEPT WE'RE NOT.
I...I DON'T UNDERSTAND...?
IT'S REALLY RATHER SIMPLE.
YOU'RE JUST THE GUINEA PIG.
WH... WHAT DO YOU MEAN?
SAY HELLO --
"-- TO ROVER!"
SENTINEL UNIT ACTIVATING HUNTER/KILLER MODE.
IDENTIFYING MUTANT BIO-PATTERN ONE.
TARGET!
F-WASH
SQWAWK
IDENTIFYING MUTANT BIO-PAT...
P-PLEASE... I ONLY CAME HERE T-TO M MEET OTHER P-PEOPLE LIKE M--ME!
PAGE 43

-- PATT <FZzK> PATT <FzZK>
--ERNSZZZZZ <FZZZK>...
WHAT JUST HAPPENED?
IT'S LIKE THE BATTERY JUST *DIED*.
ACTUALLY, IT'S
ITS CPU COULDN'T COPE WITH THE SUDDEN INFLUX OF MULTIPLE MUTANT BIOSIGNATURES ON ITS SENSORS.
NO...
THAT WOULD BE *US* BY THE WAY.
OPERATION SALVATION IS GO, GO, GO!
X-MEN — ATTACK PATTERN DELTA!
CARRIE! VERHOEVEN! KEEP THE MUTIES BUSY!
WHAT ABOUT YOU?
DON'T WORRY --
SQWAWK
-- I'M TAKING CARE OF OUR INSURANCE POLICY!
I'M TRULY SORRY, MY DEAR --

-- BUT LOGAN AND I --
-- HAVE BEEN BEATING ON PEOPLE LIKE YOU --
-- SINCE YOU WERE STILL IN PIGTAILS!
I TRUST THAT'S NOT TOO UNCOMFORTABLE.
STILL CAN'T RESIST TRYING TO IMPRESS THE PRETTY GIRLS, HUH?
I GENERALLY PREFER THE ONE'S WHO AREN'T PSYCHOTIC.
WELL, JUDGING BY THE SET UP THIS SNEIJDER GUYS GOT GOING ON...
"...HE AIN'T SO PICKY!"
GIVE US THE BOY, SNEIJDER.
NO WAY!
I'M NOT STUPID, YOU WON'T LET ANYTHING HAPPEN TO HIM.
AND WHILE I'VE GOT HIM, THIS LITTLE FREAK IS MY TICKET OUT OF HERE!
THAT'S IT!
PAGE 45

MY NAME IS BARNELL BOHUSK
WHAT...?
AND WHILE YOU MIGHT HAVE TRICKED ME --
-- I AM NOT A FREAK!!!
ARGH!
PEK
PEK
PEK
THE BOY HAS A WARRIOR'S HEART.
YOU'RE RIGHT, STORM. KID'S ALREADY GOT MORE SAND THAN SUMMERS.
PEK
PEK
PEK
ALWAYS WITH THE LOW BLOWS.
ERRR, GUYS --
SYSTEM REBOOT COMPLETE.
IDENTIFYING MUTANT BIO-PATTERNS ONE THRU FIVE.
-- I THINK WE'VE GOT A PROBLEM!
TARGET!
FWASH
WE NEED TO TAKE THIS THING DOWN... AND FAST!
IT'S GOING TO BE DIFFICULT.
THAT MODEL'S POWERED BY A NEUTRINO RELAY CORE. HIGHLY UNSTABLE...
ENGLISH, PLEASE?
GOING BY THE STATE OF ITS PROTECTIVE PLATING IF WE HIT THAT SENTINEL TOO HARD WE COULD END UP BLASTING HOLLAND OFF THE MAP!
I CAN SEE THE FLAW IN THAT PLAN.
BUT IF WE COULD FIND SOME OTHER WAY OF DEACTIVATING THE UNIT...

LIKE WHAT?
IT'S HARDLY LIKE THERE'S A BIG RED 'OFF' SWITCH JUST LYING ABOUT...
KID...
NO!!!
IDENTIFYING MUTANT BIO-PATTERN ONE.
HE'S GOING FOR SNEIJDER'S CONTROL UNIT!
STORM...
I'M ON IT!
TARGET!
F-WASH
WOOOOH!
HUFF, HUFF, HUFF
K-CHIK

IDENTIFYING MUTAAAAAa...
DID I DO GOOD?
YOU DID GOOD.
...MOBILE CEREBRO PROGRAMME ONLINE...
...MISSION PARAMETERS COMPLETED...
...LOCAL LAW ENFORCEMENT EN ROUTE ...
...UNCATALOGUED MUTANT BIO-PATTERN SAVED...
...MUTANT SUBJECT: BARNELL BOHUSK...
...X-DATABASE CODENAME GENERATED...
...CODENAME: 'BEAK'...
....'BEAK' IN TRANSIT TO XAVIER INSTITUTE...
...'BEAK' SAFE FROM HARM.
THE END.

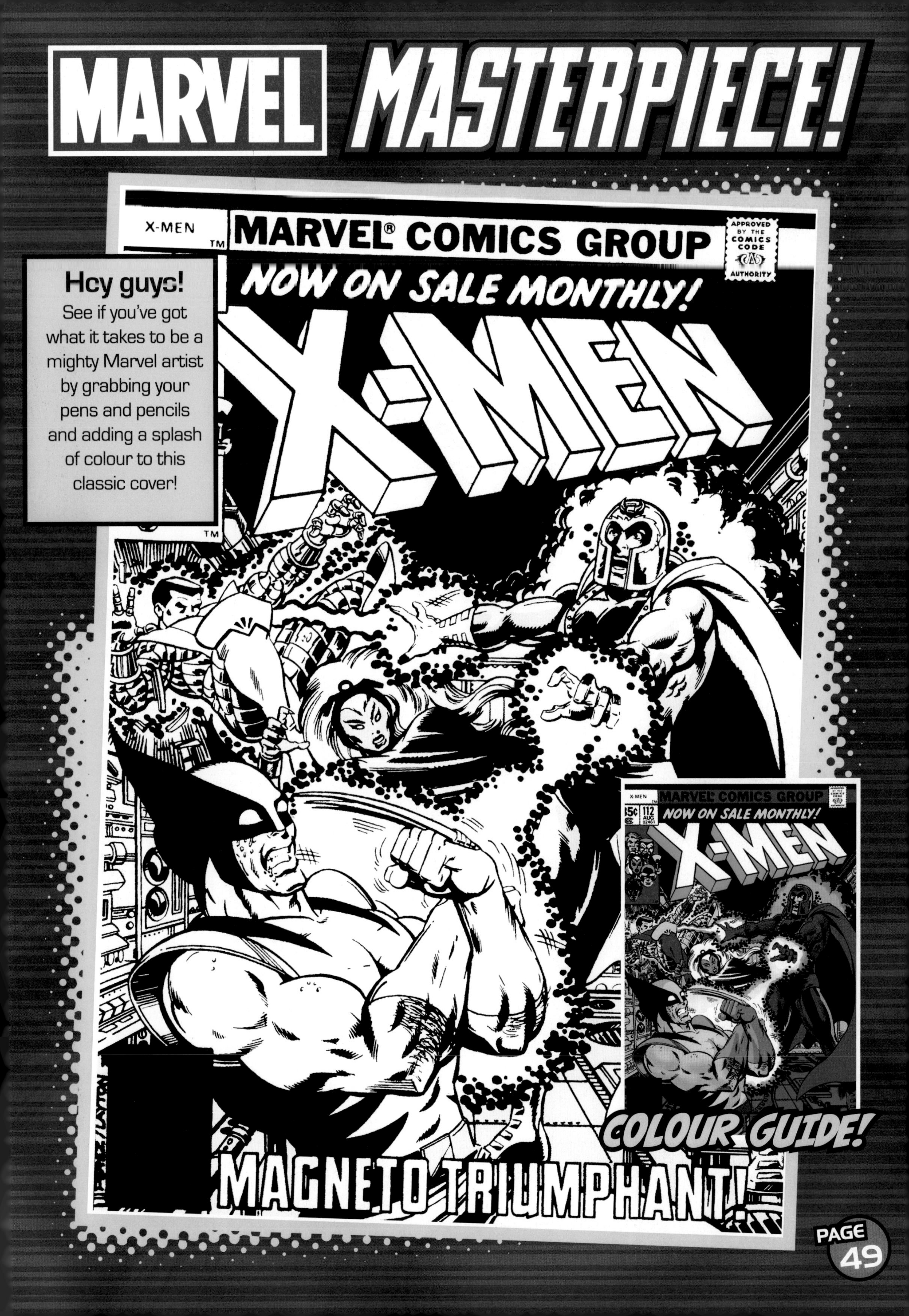
MARVEL MASTERPIECE!
X-MEN
MARVEL® COMICS GROUP
APPROVED BY THE COMICS CODE AUTHORITY
NOW ON SALE MONTHLY!
X-MEN
Hey guys!
See if you've got what it takes to be a mighty Marvel artist by grabbing your pens and pencils and adding a splash of colour to this classic cover!
MAGNETO TRIUMPHANT!
COLOUR GUIDE!
X-MEN
MARVEL COMICS GROUP
35¢ 112 AUG
NOW ON SALE MONTHLY!
X-MEN

X-MEN
THE ESSENTIAL GUIDE!

Above ground, Xavier's mansion is like any other private school with classrooms, study halls, sports grounds and dormitories for the staff and students.

To see the really interesting stuff you need to jump into one of the hidden turbo-lifts and head down to the sub-basement....

THE WAR ROOM

The **War Room** is the hub of the X-Men's operations. From here, the group plan their missions and formulate strategies to help **mutantkind.**

The room features a sophisticated computer system that constantly gathers information on **mutant activities** around the world by monitoring TV, radio and Internet news-feeds.

CEREBRO

Cerebro is housed inside a large spherical underground chamber. It was designed by **Professor X** to detect **mutant brain patterns** anywhere in the world, allowing the X-Men to instantly pinpoint the location of any who may be in danger.

INSIDE THE X-MANSION!

THE DANGER ROOM

The Danger Room is the X-Men's main training arena. Thanks to an array of **hi-tech holographic projectors**, the room can be used to simulate any combat situation, allowing the X-Men to practise new moves and hone their skills in safety.

THE X-JET HANGAR

The **X-Men's Blackbird Jet** is housed in a **secret underground hangar** beneath the school's sports area. When the Blackbird needs to get airborne, the entire roof, including the tennis courts and swimming pool above, slide back allowing the jet to take-off vertically.

THE SENTINELS

Of all the threats the X-Men face in their fight to protect mutantkind, the Sentinels are perhaps the most deadly. Read on to find out more about them!

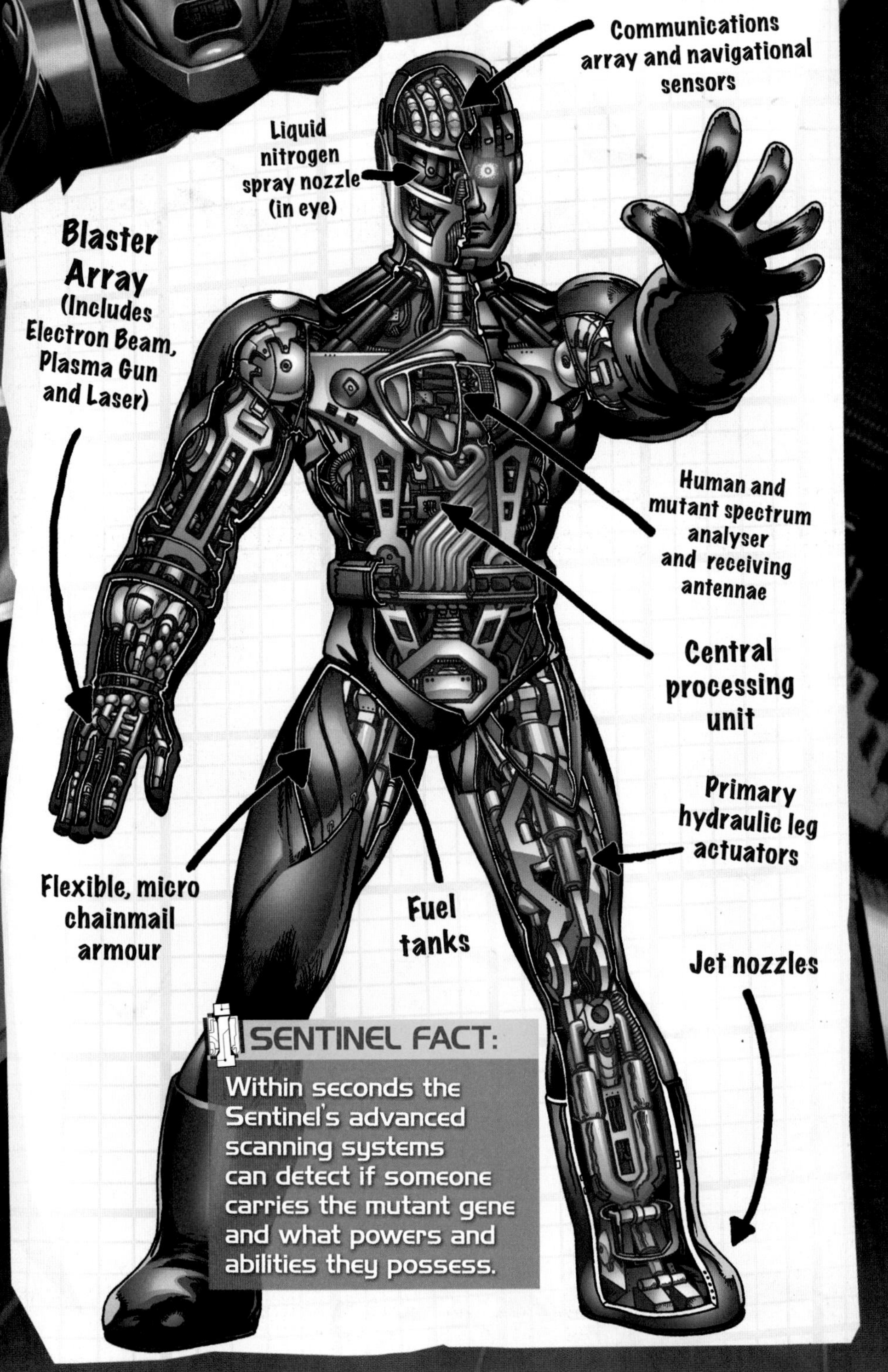

NAME: Sentinels
HEIGHT: 30'
WEIGHT: 25 tons
PRIMARY FUNCTION: To hunt and destroy mutants.

SENTINEL FACT:
The first Sentinels were created in a giant mobile factory called the Master Mold.

POWER RANKING:

STRENGTH:	15
SPEED:	9
INTELLIGENCE:	10
AGILITY:	8
POWERS:	7

SENTINEL FACT:
Within seconds the Sentinel's advanced scanning systems can detect if someone carries the mutant gene and what powers and abilities they possess.

He is a god in human form and one of the strongest heroes on the planet. Read on to find out all about...

THE MIGHTY THOR

MIGHT AND MAGIC!

Beyond this world lies the kingdom of Asgard, a mystical land inhabited by a race of noble **warriors**. Thor was regarded as their greatest champion. However, his incredible prowess and legendary status had made him **vain** and **boastful**.

A MORTAL LIFE!

To humble Thor, his father Odin **banished** him to Earth. He became Dr. Donald Blake, a mild-mannered physician who healed the sick and had no knowledge of his former life. Eventually Odin decided that Thor had learnt enough and revealed to him his **true nature**.

NAME: THOR ODINSON
HEIGHT: 6′ 6″
WEIGHT: 640 LBS
POWERS: SUPER STRENGTH, AGILITY AND TOUGHNESS, THE ABILITY TO SUMMON AND CONTROL STORMS AND DIMENSIONAL TRAVEL.

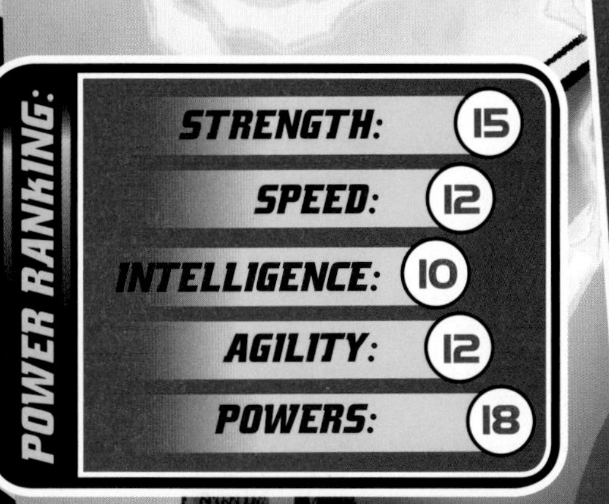

POWER RANKING:

STRENGTH:	15
SPEED:	12
INTELLIGENCE:	10
AGILITY:	12
POWERS:	18

GUARDIAN OF EARTH!

Instead of returning to Asgard, Thor decided to stay on Earth. His time as Dr. Donald Blake had taught him to **respect** human life and he vowed to become a hero – using use his ***amazing god-like powers*** to protect humankind from danger.

NOW READ ON TO SEE THE THUNDER GOD IN ACTION!

WHEN DR. DONALD BLAKE STRIKES HIS WOODEN WALKING-STICK UPON THE GROUND, IT BECOMES THE MYSTIC HAMMER MJOLNIR.
THE WAR OF THE TROLLS
SCRIPT TROLL: KIERON GILLEN ART OGRE: NEIL CAMERON
LETTERING GOBLIN: TIM WARRAN-SMITH
THE PHYSICIAN IS TRANSFORMED INTO THE NORSE GOD OF THUNDER, MASTER OF THE STORM, LORD OF THE LIVING LIGHTNING – AND HEIR TO THE THRONE OF ETERNAL ASGARD.
HE BECOMES...
THE MIGHTY THOR
OUR TALE DOESN'T BEGIN WITH THOR ON FAMILIAR EARTH – BUT IN THE MYSTICAL LAND OF GUNDERSHEIM! HOME OF THE TROLLS!
WHERE THEIR GREATEST SMITH UTARK SHOWS HIS LATEST MYSTICAL MACHINE TO THE TITANIC TROLL-CHAMPION... ULIK!
MASTER ULIK! THIS MACHINE LETS US PEER INTO THE CHATTER OF HUMANS.
UPON WHAT MORTAL KNOWLEDGE DO YOU WISH TO SPY?
ULIK! WHOM NO WARRIOR HAS EVER DEFEATED!
(EXCEPT FOR THOR.)
(AND THAT WAS A CLOSE ONE.)
LET US START WITH ME, URTAK. LET US SEE WHAT THEY THINK OF ULIK!
...
WHO IS THIS BUTCHERBUTCHER CREATURE?
WHO DARES SLANDER ULIK THE UNSTOPPABLE SO?

CB Forums
Heroes in Action > Solo Heroes > Thor
Thor's Baddies: Who's The Lamest?
Register
FAQ
Members List
Calendar
User Name
Password
ButcherButcher
Watcher!
Thor's Baddies: Who's The Lamest?
Ulik! He's not just lame. He's ultr
He sucks so hard that he's got a
job clearing drains. My GRAN is
five times as frightening as Ulik
If you tied her hand behind her
blindfolded her AND gave Ulik
BUTCHER! TAKE THE GARBAGE OUT.
JUST COMING, MA!
CAN WE FIND THIS LOATHSOME CREATURE?
YES, WITH SIGILS AND MAGIKS AND...
NO DETAILS, SMITH. OPEN THE PORTAL.
THIS IS UNBEARABLE!
NO CREATURE - GOD, NOR MAN, NOR GIANT - HAS DARED SPEAK SO!
TO MIDGARD, MY TROLLS!
TO WAR WITH THIS BUTCHERBUTCHER!

MY HONOUR MUST BE AVENGED!
THIS IS NOT GOOD.
MEANWHILE, ACROSS NEW YORK CITY...
NO MATTER WHAT YOUR GREAT-GRANDMOTHER USED TO SAY, SMEARING YOUR FACE WITH JAM ISN'T A SURE CURE FOR HEADACHES.
I'D RECOMMEND TWO PARACETAMOL, AND AN EARLY NIGHT.
DOCTOR — THIS IS INCREDIBLE! TROLLS HAVE INVADED THE SUBURBS!
THEY'LL DESPERATELY NEED DOCTORS THERE. YOU'LL EXCUSE ME.
AND REMEMBER — JAM ON BREAD NOT ON HEAD.

DONALD BLAKE CALLS FORTH THE THUNDER-GOD AND RUSHES ACROSS THE CITY TO FIND ULIK VENTING HIS WRATH NOT UPON A SUPERHUMAN FOE – BUT A SUBURBAN HOUSEHOLD.
ULIK – STILL YOUR HAND!
THIS IS SOOO NOT GOOD.
KRA-CHOOM!
THE GREAT WARRIORS OF THE TROLLS MENACING HUMAN CHILDREN?
THIS IS A DISGRACE!
DISGRACE IT IS, BUT IT IS NOT ULIK'S.
FOUL LIES HAVE BEEN UTTERED!
AND ULIK MUST HAVE SATISFACTION!
MASTER ULIK!
WE'VE FOUND HER!

AT LAST.
KEEP THOR FROM ME, BROTHERS.
I WILL CORRECT THE MISAPPREHENSION.
THE WORLD WILL KNOW THAT IT IS ULIK OF GUNDERSHEIM NOT THE GRANDMOTHER OF BUTCHERBUTCHER WHO IS MOST FEARSOME!
SO YOU'RE THE ONE IN CHARGE OF THIS RABBLE?
ALL THOSE SCALY-FELLOWS CAME TRAMPING INTO MY FRONT ROOM WITH THEIR MUCKY FEET! OH, THOSE STAINS.
AND THERE'S NO WALL ANY MORE! WHAT'S GOING TO HAPPEN WITH MY HEATING BILL NOW THERE'S A TROLL-SHAPED HOLE IN MY POOR LITTLE WALL?
DESTROYING A DEAR OLD LADY'S HOUSE IN ONE OF YOUR EXTRADIMENSIONAL RAMPAGES!
I'VE NEVER SEEN THE LIKE! YOU SHOULD BE ASHAMED OF YOURSELF! SHAME!
POKE
HMM. PERHAPS THERE WAS SOME TRUTH IN THAT ONE ACCUSATION, BUTCHERBUTCHER -
- BUT THERE ARE MANY MORE OTHER INSULTS WHICH ULIK MUST REFUTE!

NAY!
THOR! ARE YOU DERANGED?
IT IS YOU WHO ARE DERANGED ULIK, TO THINK THOR WOULD STAND ASIDE WHEN AN INNOCENT CHILD IS THREATENED!
NO INNOCENT HE! HIS WORDS ARE POISON!
I CANNOT BEAR HIS INSULTS!
I CANNOT BELIEVE YOU FOOLISH ENOUGH TO PROTECT SUCH A KNAVE.
THE PROTECTION OF ALL IS THOR'S DUTY!
DO NOT DARE MOCK IT!
FZT-ZAP!
EVEN WHEN HE SPEAKS SIMILARLY ABOUT YOU?
TO DEFEND THOSE WHO SLANDER YOU IS LUNACY!
WHAT SAYEST THOU?

URTAK - TELL HIM!
I QUOTETH FROM THE "HEROES IN ACTION FORUM" WHERE BUTCHERBUTCHER DID SAY:
"OF COURSE THOR ONLY GETS LAME VILLAINS COZ HE'S SO LAME HIMSELF. HULK'S ENEMIES? THEY'D WHUP HIM. IRON MAN'S? THEY'D WHUP HIM. EVEN ANT-MAN'S WOULD HAVE HIM!"
THIS INVECTIVE CONTINUES FOR SEVERAL PAGES, SIRE.
DIDST THOU?
I'MSORRYI'MSORRY I'MSORRY.
I DIDN'T REALISE I'D HURT ANYONE'S FEELINGS. AND I DIDN'T KNOW WHAT YOU WERE REALLY LIKE. I MEAN THOR — YOU SAVED ME. THAT WAS INCREDIBLE.
AND ULIK, YOU TOTALLY ANNIHILATED MY NEIGHBOURHOOD.
THAT'S SOOOO COOOOL.
I'M SORRY.
THOR'S HONOUR IS SATISFIED. BUT WHAT OF ULIK'S?
THIS REGRET IS PLEASING TO THE TROLLS - BUT THE INSULT WAS GRAVE.
WE DEMAND REPARATIONS! PRECIOUS POSSESSIONS TO GILD THE HALLS OF GUNDERSHEIM! WE DEMAND RICHES!
PAGE 60

B-BUT — I'VE ONLY GOT TEN DOLLARS IN THE BANK.
YOU COULD GIVE MR ULIK THAT VIDEOGAME I GOT YOU YOUR LAST BIRTHDAY.
AW, GRAN!
AH - THE LOSS CAUSES PAIN TO THE TINY HUMAN. SPLENDID. THIS "VIDEOGAME" WILL BE SUFFICIENT TO SALVE THE HURT OF ULIK.
AND SO THE PEACE WAS MADE BETWEEN ULIK OF GUNDERSHEIM AND BUTCHERBUTCHER OF JUST OUTSIDE NEW YORK.
(AFTER URTAK FIXED UP THE NEIGHBOURHOOD. STARTING WITH GRAN'S HOUSE.)
BUT SOME WEEKS LATER — THE CRIES OF ULIK ONCE AGAIN ROCK GUNDERSHEIM'S TUNNELS.
NO! THIS IS IMPOSSIBLE! ULIK IS THE STRONGEST!
ULIK IS THE MIGHIEST! ULIK IS UNDEFEATABLE!
BUTCHERBUTCHER 15
UliKistHemIGhtiESt: -1
MAN, YOU MAY BE, BUT YOU TOTALLY SUCK AT CALL OF WAR 5!
PERHAPS ULIK IS LULLING YOU INTO A FALSE SENSE OF SECURITY, MORTAL.
FOR ULIK WILL HAVE HIS REVENGE!
THE END?

ANSWERS
ULTIMATE X-CHANGE!
PAGE 19
X-TRAORDINARY POWER!
PAGE 41
X-MANSION ASSAULT!
PAGE 33